Great Is Thy Faithfulness

NEW MORNING, NEW MERCIES

16-Month Weekly Pocket Planner with Bible Ready Reference
2011–2012

His compas...
morni...
La...

2012

January						
S	M	T	W	T	F	S
1	2	3	4	5	6	7
8	9	10	11	12	13	14
15	16	17	18	19	20	21
22	23	24	25	26	27	28
29	30	31				

February						
S	M	T	W	T	F	S
			1	2	3	4
5	6	7	8	9	10	11
12	13	14	15	16	17	18
19	20	21	22	23	24	25
26	27	28	29			

March						
S	M	T	W	T	F	S
				1	2	3
4	5	6	7	8	9	10
11	12	13	14	15	16	17
18	19	20	21	22	23	24
25	26	27	28	29	30	31

April						
S	M	T	W	T	F	S
1	2	3	4	5	6	7
8	9	10	11	12	13	14
15	16	17	18	19	20	21
22	23	24	25	26	27	28
29	30					

May						
S	M	T	W	T	F	S
		1	2	3	4	5
6	7	8	9	10	11	12
13	14	15	16	17	18	19
20	21	22	23	24	25	26
27	28	29	30	31		

June						
S	M	T	W	T	F	S
					1	2
3	4	5	6	7	8	9
10	11	12	13	14	15	16
17	18	19	20	21	22	23
24	25	26	27	28	29	30

July						
S	M	T	W	T	F	S
1	2	3	4	5	6	7
8	9	10	11	12	13	14
15	16	17	18	19	20	21
22	23	24	25	26	27	28
29	30	31				

August						
S	M	T	W	T	F	S
			1	2	3	4
5	6	7	8	9	10	11
12	13	14	15	16	17	18
19	20	21	22	23	24	25
26	27	28	29	30	31	

September						
S	M	T	W	T	F	S
						1
2	3	4	5	6	7	8
9	10	11	12	13	14	15
16	17	18	19	20	21	22
23	24	25	26	27	28	29
30						

October						
S	M	T	W	T	F	S
	1	2	3	4	5	6
7	8	9	10	11	12	13
14	15	16	17	18	19	20
21	22	23	24	25	26	27
28	29	30	31			

November						
S	M	T	W	T	F	S
				1	2	3
4	5	6	7	8	9	10
11	12	13	14	15	16	17
18	19	20	21	22	23	24
25	26	27	28	29	30	

December						
S	M	T	W	T	F	S
						1
2	3	4	5	6	7	8
9	10	11	12	13	14	15
16	17	18	19	20	21	22
23	24	25	26	27	28	29
30	31					

Scriptures of Hope and Comfort

God has said, "Never will I leave you; never will I forsake you." So we say with confidence, "The Lord is my helper; I will not be afraid."
Hebrews 13:5–6 NIV

For I am sure that neither death nor life, nor angels nor rulers, nor things present nor things to come, nor powers, nor height nor depth, nor anything else in all creation, will be able to separate us from the love of God in Christ Jesus our Lord.
Romans 8:38–39

[Jesus said,] "Come to me, all you who are weary and burdened, and I will give you rest. Take my yoke upon you and learn from me, for I am gentle and humble in heart, and you will find rest for your souls. For my yoke is easy and my burden is light."
Matthew 11:28–30 NIV

My God will meet all your needs according to his glorious riches in Christ Jesus.
Philippians 4:19 NIV

If God is for us, who can be against us? He who did not spare his own Son but gave him up for us all, how will he not also with him graciously give us all things?
Romans 8:31–32

Jesus said to her, "I am the resurrection and the life. Whoever believes in me, though he die, yet shall he live, and everyone who lives and believes in me shall never die."
John 11:25–26

SEPTEMBER 2011

1 THURSDAY

2 FRIDAY

3 SATURDAY

*Because of the LORD's great love we are
not consumed, for his compassions never fail.
They are new every morning.*

Lamentations 3:22–23 NIV

4 SUNDAY

5 MONDAY–LABOR DAY

6 TUESDAY

PRAYER REQUESTS AND THANKSGIVING

7 WEDNESDAY

8 THURSDAY

9 FRIDAY

10 SATURDAY

September 2011

11 Sunday—Patriot Day
Grandparents Day

12 Monday

13 Tuesday

Prayer Requests and Thanksgiving

*Let your face shine on your servant;
save me in your unfailing love.*
Psalm 31:16 NIV

14 WEDNESDAY

15 THURSDAY

16 FRIDAY

17 SATURDAY

SEPTEMBER 2011

18 SUNDAY—CATECHETICAL SUNDAY

19 MONDAY

20 TUESDAY

PRAYER REQUESTS AND THANKSGIVING

21 WEDNESDAY

22 THURSDAY

23 FRIDAY—AUTUMN BEGINS

24 SATURDAY

SEPTEMBER 2011

25 SUNDAY

26 MONDAY

27 TUESDAY

PRAYER REQUESTS AND THANKSGIVING

*Fight the good fight of the faith. Take hold
of the eternal life to which you were called.*
1 Timothy 6:12

28 WEDNESDAY—SEE YOU AT THE POLE

29 THURSDAY—ROSH HASHANAH

30 FRIDAY—ROSH HASHANAH

1 SATURDAY

OCTOBER 2011

2 SUNDAY

NATIONAL LIFE CHAIN SUNDAY

3 MONDAY

4 TUESDAY

PRAYER REQUESTS AND THANKSGIVING

> The works of his hands are faithful and just; all his precepts are trustworthy. They are steadfast for ever and ever, done in faithfulness and uprightness.
> Psalm 111:7–8 NIV

5 WEDNESDAY

6 THURSDAY

7 FRIDAY

8 SATURDAY—YOM KIPPUR

OCTOBER 2011

PASTOR APPRECIATION MONTH
RESPECT LIFE MONTH

10 MONDAY— COLUMBUS DAY (OBSERVED)
THANKSGIVING DAY (CANADA)

11 TUESDAY

PRAYER REQUESTS AND THANKSGIVING

12 WEDNESDAY

13 THURSDAY

14 FRIDAY

15 SATURDAY

OCTOBER 2011

16 SUNDAY

PASTOR APPRECIATION MONTH
RESPECT LIFE MONTH

NATIONAL BOSS DAY
NATIONAL SUNDAY SCHOOL TEACHERS DAY

17 MONDAY

18 TUESDAY

PRAYER REQUESTS AND THANKSGIVING

*A faithful God who does no wrong,
upright and just is he.*
Deuteronomy 32:4 NIV

19 WEDNESDAY

20 THURSDAY

21 FRIDAY

22 SATURDAY

October 2011

23 SUNDAY

24 MONDAY

25 TUESDAY

PRAYER REQUESTS AND THANKSGIVING

26 WEDNESDAY

27 THURSDAY

28 FRIDAY

29 SATURDAY

30 SUNDAY

31 MONDAY— HALLOWEEN
REFORMATION DAY

1 TUESDAY— ALL SAINTS' DAY

PRAYER REQUESTS AND THANKSGIVING

He loves righteousness and justice;
The earth is full of the goodness of the LORD.
Psalm 33:5 NKJV

2 WEDNESDAY

3 THURSDAY

4 FRIDAY

5 SATURDAY

6 SUNDAY—Daylight Savings Time Ends

7 MONDAY

8 TUESDAY—Election Day

PRAYER REQUESTS AND THANKSGIVING

May the LORD give strength to his people!
May the LORD bless his people with peace!
Psalm 29:11

9 WEDNESDAY

10 THURSDAY

11 FRIDAY— VETERANS DAY
REMEMBRANCE DAY (CANADA)

12 SATURDAY

November 2011

13 SUNDAY— INTERNATIONAL DAY OF PRAYER
FOR THE PERSECUTED CHURCH

14 MONDAY

15 TUESDAY

PRAYER REQUESTS AND THANKSGIVING

16 WEDNESDAY

17 THURSDAY

18 FRIDAY

19 SATURDAY

November 2011

20 SUNDAY— NATIONAL BIBLE WEEK
(ENDS NOV. 27)

21 MONDAY

22 TUESDAY

PRAYER REQUESTS AND THANKSGIVING

Give thanks to the LORD, for he is good;
for his steadfast love endures forever!
1 Chronicles 16:34

23 WEDNESDAY

24 THURSDAY—THANKSGIVING DAY

25 FRIDAY

26 SATURDAY

27 SUNDAY— ADVENT BEGINS

28 MONDAY

29 TUESDAY

PRAYER REQUESTS AND THANKSGIVING

*I have spoken of your faithfulness and your salvation;
    I have not concealed your steadfast love and your
faithfulness from the great congregation. (Psalm 40:10)*

30 WEDNESDAY

1 THURSDAY

2 FRIDAY

3 SATURDAY

DECEMBER 2011

4 SUNDAY

5 MONDAY

6 TUESDAY

PRAYER REQUESTS AND THANKSGIVING

This is the day that the LORD has made;
let us rejoice and be glad in it.
Psalm 118:24

7 WEDNESDAY

8 THURSDAY

9 FRIDAY

10 SATURDAY

December 2011

11 Sunday

12 Monday

13 Tuesday

Prayer Requests and Thanksgiving

14 WEDNESDAY

15 THURSDAY

16 FRIDAY

17 SATURDAY

DECEMBER 2011

18 SUNDAY

19 MONDAY

20 TUESDAY

PRAYER REQUESTS AND THANKSGIVING

Every good and perfect gift is from above, coming down from the Father of the heavenly lights, who does not change like shifting shadows. (James 1:17 NIV)

21 WEDNESDAY—HANUKKAH BEGINS

22 THURSDAY—WINTER BEGINS

23 FRIDAY

24 SATURDAY—CHRISTMAS EVE

December 2011

25 SUNDAY—Christmas Day

26 MONDAY— Kwanzaa Begins
BOXING DAY (Canada)

27 TUESDAY

PRAYER REQUESTS AND THANKSGIVING

> God, who said, "Let light shine out of darkness," made his light shine in our hearts to give us the light of the knowledge of the glory of God in the face of Christ. (2 Corinthians 4:6 NIV)

28 WEDNESDAY

29 THURSDAY

30 FRIDAY

31 SATURDAY—NEW YEAR'S EVE

JANUARY 2012

1 SUNDAY—NEW YEAR'S DAY

2 MONDAY

3 TUESDAY

PRAYER REQUESTS AND THANKSGIVING

*Jesus Christ is the same yesterday
and today and forever.*
Hebrews 13:8

4 WEDNESDAY

5 THURSDAY

6 FRIDAY—EPIPHANY

7 SATURDAY

8 SUNDAY

9 MONDAY

10 TUESDAY

PRAYER REQUESTS AND THANKSGIVING

I will sing of your strength; I will sing aloud of your steadfast love in the morning. For you have been to me a fortress and a refuge in the day of my distress. (Psalm 59:16)

11 WEDNESDAY

12 THURSDAY

13 FRIDAY

14 SATURDAY

JANUARY 2012

15 SUNDAY—Sanctity of Human Life Week

16 MONDAY— Martin Luther King Day
(Observed)

17 TUESDAY

PRAYER REQUESTS AND THANKSGIVING

I have redeemed you;
I have called you by name, you are mine.
Isaiah 43:1

18 WEDNESDAY

19 THURSDAY

20 FRIDAY

21 SATURDAY

JANUARY 2012

22 SUNDAY

23 MONDAY

24 TUESDAY

PRAYER REQUESTS AND THANKSGIVING

25 WEDNESDAY

26 THURSDAY

27 FRIDAY

28 SATURDAY

FEBRUARY 2012

29 SUNDAY—Catholic Schools Week

30 MONDAY

31 TUESDAY

PRAYER REQUESTS AND THANKSGIVING

*Now the God of hope fill you with all joy
and peace in believing.*
Romans 15:13 KJV

1 WEDNESDAY

2 THURSDAY

3 FRIDAY

4 SATURDAY

FEBRUARY 2012

5 SUNDAY—BOY SCOUT SUNDAY

6 MONDAY

7 TUESDAY

PRAYER REQUESTS AND THANKSGIVING

That you, being rooted and grounded in love, may have strength to comprehend with all the saints what is the breadth and length and height and depth, and to know the love of Christ. (Ephesians 3:17–19)

8 WEDNESDAY

9 THURSDAY

10 FRIDAY

11 SATURDAY

FEBRUARY 2012

BLACK HISTORY MONTH

12 SUNDAY—LINCOLN'S BIRTHDAY

13 MONDAY

14 TUESDAY—VALENTINE'S DAY

PRAYER REQUESTS AND THANKSGIVING

15 WEDNESDAY

16 THURSDAY

17 FRIDAY

18 SATURDAY

FEBRUARY 2012

19 SUNDAY

20 MONDAY— PRESIDENTS DAY/
WASHINGTON'S B-DAY
(OBSERVED)

21 TUESDAY

PRAYER REQUESTS AND THANKSGIVING

Turn, O Lord, and deliver me;
save me because of your unfailing love.
Psalm 6:4 NIV

22 WEDNESDAY— ASH WEDNESDAY
LENT BEGINS

23 THURSDAY

24 FRIDAY

25 SATURDAY

FEBRUARY 2012

26 SUNDAY

27 MONDAY

28 TUESDAY

PRAYER REQUESTS AND THANKSGIVING

29 WEDNESDAY

1 THURSDAY

2 FRIDAY—WORLD DAY OF PRAYER

3 SATURDAY

MARCH 2012

4 SUNDAY—LUTHERAN SCHOOLS WEEK

5 MONDAY

6 TUESDAY

PRAYER REQUESTS AND THANKSGIVING

*Now the Lord of peace himself
give you peace always.*
2 Thessalonians 3:16 KJV

7 WEDNESDAY

8 THURSDAY

9 FRIDAY—WORLD DAY OF PRAYER

10 SATURDAY

MARCH 2012

11 SUNDAY— DAYLIGHT SAVINGS TIME BEGINS
GIRL SCOUT SUNDAY

12 MONDAY

13 TUESDAY

PRAYER REQUESTS AND THANKSGIVING

*Where morning dawns and evening fades
you call forth songs of joy.*
Psalm 65:8 NIV

14 WEDNESDAY

15 THURSDAY

16 FRIDAY

17 SATURDAY—ST. PATRICK'S DAY

MARCH 2012

18 SUNDAY

19 MONDAY

20 TUESDAY—SPRING BEGINS

PRAYER REQUESTS AND THANKSGIVING

*Satisfy us in the morning with your steadfast love,
that we may rejoice and be glad all our days.*
Psalm 90:14

21 WEDNESDAY

22 THURSDAY

23 FRIDAY

24 SATURDAY

25 SUNDAY

26 MONDAY

27 TUESDAY

PRAYER REQUESTS AND THANKSGIVING

*You have granted me life and steadfast love,
and your care has preserved my spirit.*
Job 10:12

28 WEDNESDAY

29 THURSDAY

30 FRIDAY

31 SATURDAY

APRIL 2012

1 SUNDAY— APRIL FOOL'S DAY
PALM SUNDAY

2 MONDAY

3 TUESDAY

PRAYER REQUESTS AND THANKSGIVING

4 WEDNESDAY

5 THURSDAY—MAUNDY THURSDAY

6 FRIDAY—GOOD FRIDAY

7 SATURDAY—PASSOVER

APRIL 2012

8 SUNDAY— EASTER SUNDAY

9 MONDAY

10 TUESDAY

PRAYER REQUESTS AND THANKSGIVING

Now to him who is able to do far more abundantly than all that we ask or think, according to the power at work within us, to him be glory in the church and in Christ Jesus throughout all generations. (Ephesians 3:20–21)

11 WEDNESDAY

12 THURSDAY

13 FRIDAY

14 SATURDAY

15 SUNDAY— NATIONAL VOLUNTEER WEEK
INCOME TAX DUE

16 MONDAY

17 TUESDAY

PRAYER REQUESTS AND THANKSGIVING

> *"Though the mountains be shaken and the hills be removed, yet my unfailing love for you will not be shaken nor my covenant of peace be removed," says the LORD, who has compassion on you.* (Isaiah 54:10 NIV)

18 WEDNESDAY

19 THURSDAY

20 FRIDAY

21 SATURDAY

APRIL 2012

22 SUNDAY— ADMINISTRATIVE PROFESSIONALS WEEK
EARTH DAY

23 MONDAY

24 TUESDAY

PRAYER REQUESTS AND THANKSGIVING

*The grace of our Lord overflowed for me
with the faith and love that are in Christ Jesus.*
1 Timothy 1:14

25 WEDNESDAY—ADMIN. PROF. DAY

26 THURSDAY—DAUGHTERS TO WORK DAY

27 FRIDAY

28 SATURDAY

MAY 2012

29 SUNDAY

30 MONDAY

1 TUESDAY

PRAYER REQUESTS AND THANKSGIVING

At an acceptable time, O God, in the abundance of your steadfast love answer me in your saving faithfulness. (Psalm 69:13)

2 WEDNESDAY

3 THURSDAY—NATIONAL DAY OF PRAYER

4 FRIDAY

5 SATURDAY—CINCO DE MAYO

MAY 2012

6 SUNDAY—National Teacher
Appreciation Week

7 MONDAY

8 TUESDAY—Teacher's Day

PRAYER REQUESTS AND THANKSGIVING

*That Christ may dwell in your
hearts through faith.*
Ephesians 3:17 NIV

9 WEDNESDAY

10 THURSDAY

11 FRIDAY

12 SATURDAY

MAY 2012

13 SUNDAY—MOTHER'S DAY

14 MONDAY

15 TUESDAY

PRAYER REQUESTS AND THANKSGIVING

*Grace be to you and peace from God
our Father, and from the Lord Jesus Christ.*
2 Corinthians 1:2 KJV

16 WEDNESDAY

17 THURSDAY—ASCENSION DAY

18 FRIDAY

19 SATURDAY—ARMED FORCES DAY

MAY 2012

20 SUNDAY

21 MONDAY—Victoria Day (Canada)

22 TUESDAY

PRAYER REQUESTS AND THANKSGIVING

*God is our refuge and strength,
a very present help in trouble.*
Psalm 46:1 KJV

23 WEDNESDAY

24 THURSDAY

25 FRIDAY

26 SATURDAY

MAY 2012

27 SUNDAY—PENTECOST

28 MONDAY—MEMORIAL DAY (OBSERVED)

29 TUESDAY

PRAYER REQUESTS AND THANKSGIVING

My presence will go with you,
and I will give you rest.
Exodus 33:14

30 WEDNESDAY

31 THURSDAY

1 FRIDAY

2 SATURDAY

JUNE 2012

3 SUNDAY—TRINITY SUNDAY

4 MONDAY

5 TUESDAY

PRAYER REQUESTS AND THANKSGIVING

> You were not redeemed with corruptible things, like silver or gold, from your aimless conduct received by tradition from your fathers, but with the precious blood of Christ. *(1 Peter 1:18–19 NKJV)*

6 WEDNESDAY

7 THURSDAY

8 FRIDAY

9 SATURDAY

JUNE 2012

10 SUNDAY

11 MONDAY

12 TUESDAY

PRAYER REQUESTS AND THANKSGIVING

Let the beloved of the LORD rest secure in him,
for he shields him all day long.
Deuteronomy 33:12 NIV

13 WEDNESDAY

14 THURSDAY—FLAG DAY

15 FRIDAY

16 SATURDAY

JUNE 2012

17 SUNDAY—FATHER'S DAY

18 MONDAY

19 TUESDAY

PRAYER REQUESTS AND THANKSGIVING

He alone is my rock and my salvation;
he is my fortress, I will never be shaken.
Psalm 62:2 NIV

20 WEDNESDAY—SUMMER BEGINS

21 THURSDAY

22 FRIDAY

23 SATURDAY

JUNE 2012

24 SUNDAY

25 MONDAY

26 TUESDAY

PRAYER REQUESTS AND THANKSGIVING

Keep steady my steps according to your promise,
and let no iniquity get dominion over me.
Psalm 119:133

27 WEDNESDAY

28 THURSDAY

29 FRIDAY

30 SATURDAY

JULY 2012

1 SUNDAY—CANADA DAY

2 MONDAY

3 TUESDAY

PRAYER REQUESTS AND THANKSGIVING

I will sing aloud of your steadfast love in the morning. For you have been to me a fortress and a refuge in the day of my distress. (Psalm 59:16)

4 WEDNESDAY–INDEPENDENCE DAY

5 THURSDAY

6 FRIDAY

7 SATURDAY

JULY 2012

8 SUNDAY

9 MONDAY

10 TUESDAY

PRAYER REQUESTS AND THANKSGIVING

11 WEDNESDAY

12 THURSDAY

13 FRIDAY

14 SATURDAY

JULY 2012

15 SUNDAY

16 MONDAY

17 TUESDAY

PRAYER REQUESTS AND THANKSGIVING

*God will send out his steadfast
love and his faithfulness!
Psalm 57:3*

18 WEDNESDAY

19 THURSDAY

20 FRIDAY

21 SATURDAY

JULY 2012

22 SUNDAY

23 MONDAY

24 TUESDAY

PRAYER REQUESTS AND THANKSGIVING

*This hope we have as an anchor of the soul,
both sure and steadfast.*
Hebrews 6:19 NKJV

25 WEDNESDAY

26 THURSDAY

27 FRIDAY

28 SATURDAY

29 SUNDAY

30 MONDAY

31 TUESDAY

PRAYER REQUESTS AND THANKSGIVING

We know that all things work together for good to them that love God, to them who are the called according to his purpose. (Romans 8:28 KJV)

1 WEDNESDAY

2 THURSDAY

3 FRIDAY

4 SATURDAY

5 SUNDAY

6 MONDAY

7 TUESDAY

PRAYER REQUESTS AND THANKSGIVING

8 WEDNESDAY

9 THURSDAY

10 FRIDAY

11 SATURDAY

12 SUNDAY

13 MONDAY

14 TUESDAY

PRAYER REQUESTS AND THANKSGIVING

15 WEDNESDAY

16 THURSDAY

17 FRIDAY

18 SATURDAY

19 SUNDAY

20 MONDAY

21 TUESDAY

PRAYER REQUESTS AND THANKSGIVING

22 WEDNESDAY

23 THURSDAY

24 FRIDAY

25 SATURDAY

26 SUNDAY

27 MONDAY

28 TUESDAY

PRAYER REQUESTS AND THANKSGIVING

29 WEDNESDAY

30 THURSDAY

31 FRIDAY

1 SATURDAY

2 SUNDAY

3 MONDAY—LABOR DAY

4 TUESDAY

PRAYER REQUESTS AND THANKSGIVING

> *I will sing of the steadfast love of the LORD, forever; with my mouth I will make known your faithfulness to all generations. (Psalm 89:1)*

5 WEDNESDAY

6 THURSDAY

7 FRIDAY

8 SATURDAY

SEPTEMBER 2012

9 SUNDAY—GRANDPARENTS DAY

10 MONDAY

11 TUESDAY—PATRIOT DAY

PRAYER REQUESTS AND THANKSGIVING

O LORD, be gracious to us; we wait for you.
Be our arm every morning, our salvation in the
time of trouble. (Isaiah 33:2)

12 WEDNESDAY

13 THURSDAY

14 FRIDAY

15 SATURDAY

SEPTEMBER 2012

16 SUNDAY—CATECHETICAL SUNDAY

17 MONDAY—ROSH HASHANAH

18 TUESDAY—ROSH HASHANAH

PRAYER REQUESTS AND THANKSGIVING

If we confess our sins, he is faithful and just to forgive us our sins and to cleanse us from all unrighteousness. (1 John 1:9)

19 WEDNESDAY

20 THURSDAY

21 FRIDAY

22 SATURDAY—AUTUMN BEGINS

23 Sunday

24 Monday

25 Tuesday

Prayer Requests and Thanksgiving

26 WEDNESDAY— YOM KIPPUR
SEE YOU AT THE POLE

27 THURSDAY

28 FRIDAY

29 SATURDAY—AUTUMN BEGINS

OCTOBER 2012

30 SUNDAY

1 MONDAY

2 TUESDAY

PRAYER REQUESTS AND THANKSGIVING

*Let those who suffer according to God's will entrust
their souls to a faithful Creator while doing good.*
1 Peter 4:19

3 WEDNESDAY

4 THURSDAY

5 FRIDAY

6 SATURDAY

OCTOBER 2012

7 SUNDAY
NATIONAL LIFE CHAIN SUNDAY

8 MONDAY— COLUMBUS DAY (OBSERVED)
THANKSGIVING DAY (CANADA)

9 TUESDAY

PRAYER REQUESTS AND THANKSGIVING

10 WEDNESDAY

11 THURSDAY

12 FRIDAY

13 SATURDAY

OCTOBER 2012

14 SUNDAY

> *PASTOR APPRECIATION MONTH*
> *RESPECT LIFE MONTH*

15 MONDAY

16 TUESDAY—NATIONAL BOSS DAY

PRAYER REQUESTS AND THANKSGIVING

Return to the LORD your God, for he is gracious
and merciful, slow to anger, and abounding
in steadfast love. (Joel 2:13)

17 WEDNESDAY

18 THURSDAY

19 FRIDAY

20 SATURDAY

OCTOBER 2012

21 SUNDAY

NATIONAL SUNDAY SCHOOL TEACHERS DAY

22 MONDAY

23 TUESDAY

PRAYER REQUESTS AND THANKSGIVING

24 WEDNESDAY

25 THURSDAY

26 FRIDAY

27 SATURDAY

OCTOBER 2012

28 SUNDAY

29 MONDAY

30 TUESDAY

PRAYER REQUESTS AND THANKSGIVING

Let the peace of God rule in your hearts.
Colossians 3:15 KJV

31 WEDNESDAY—HALLOWEEN
REFORMATION DAY

1 THURSDAY—ALL SAINTS' DAY

2 FRIDAY

3 SATURDAY

November 2012

4 SUNDAY—Daylight Savings Time Ends

5 MONDAY

6 TUESDAY—Election Day

PRAYER REQUESTS AND THANKSGIVING

O LORD, be gracious to us; we long for you.
Be our strength every morning, our salvation in
time of distress. (Isaiah 33:2 NIV)

7 WEDNESDAY

8 THURSDAY

9 FRIDAY

10 SATURDAY

November 2012

11 SUNDAY— REMEMBRANCE DAY (CANADA)
VETERANS DAY
INTERNATIONAL DAY OF PRAYER
FOR THE PERSECUTED CHURCH

12 MONDAY

13 TUESDAY—ELECTION DAY

PRAYER REQUESTS AND THANKSGIVING

14 WEDNESDAY

15 THURSDAY

16 FRIDAY

17 SATURDAY

November 2012

18 SUNDAY—National Bible Week

19 MONDAY

20 TUESDAY

PRAYER REQUESTS AND THANKSGIVING

As you therefore have received Christ Jesus the LORD, so walk in Him,
rooted and built up in Him and established in the faith, as you have
been taught, abounding in it with thanksgiving. (Colossians 2:6–7 NKJV)

21 WEDNESDAY

22 THURSDAY—THANKSGIVING DAY

23 FRIDAY

24 SATURDAY

November 2012

25 SUNDAY

26 MONDAY

27 TUESDAY

PRAYER REQUESTS AND THANKSGIVING

The LORD, the LORD, a God merciful and gracious, slow to anger, and abounding in steadfast love and faithfulness. (Exodus 34:6–7)

28 WEDNESDAY

29 THURSDAY

30 FRIDAY

1 SATURDAY

DECEMBER 2012

2 SUNDAY—ADVENT BEGINS

3 MONDAY

4 TUESDAY

PRAYER REQUESTS AND THANKSGIVING

He will stand and shepherd his flock in the strength of the LORD, in the majesty of the name of the LORD his God. And they will live securely, for then his greatness will reach to the ends of the earth. (Micah 5:4 NIV)

5 WEDNESDAY

6 THURSDAY

7 FRIDAY

8 SATURDAY

9 SUNDAY—HANUKKAH BEGINS

10 MONDAY

11 TUESDAY

PRAYER REQUESTS AND THANKSGIVING

When the goodness and loving kindness of God our Savior appeared, he saved us.
Titus 3:4–5

12 WEDNESDAY

13 THURSDAY

14 FRIDAY

15 SATURDAY

DECEMBER 2012

16 SUNDAY

17 MONDAY

18 TUESDAY

PRAYER REQUESTS AND THANKSGIVING

This is the LORD; we have waited for him,
we will be glad and rejoice in his salvation.
Isaiah 25:9 KJV

19 WEDNESDAY

20 THURSDAY

21 FRIDAY—Winter Begins

22 SATURDAY

DECEMBER 2012

23 SUNDAY

24 MONDAY—Christmas Eve

25 TUESDAY—Christmas Day

PRAYER REQUESTS AND THANKSGIVING

There is one God, and there is one mediator between God and men, the man Christ Jesus, who gave himself as a ransom for all. (1 Timothy 2:5–6)

26 WEDNESDAY—KWANZAA BEGINS
BOXING DAY (CANADA)

27 THURSDAY

28 FRIDAY

29 SATURDAY

DECEMBER 2012

30 SUNDAY

31 MONDAY—NEW YEAR'S EVE

1 TUESDAY—NEW YEAR'S DAY

In your unfailing love you will lead the people you have redeemed. In your strength you will guide them to your holy dwelling. (Exodus 15:13 NIV)

BIBLE READY REFERENCE

Here are texts you may find helpful, both personally and when you are serving others in Jesus' name.

In times of anger	Ephesians 4:31–32
Feeling anxious	Psalm 46; Philippians 4:13
Needing confidence	Hebrews 4:16; Isaiah 26:4
For courage	2 Corinthians 1:3–7; Joshua 1:9
When in danger	Psalm 91
In discouragement	Psalm 73:23–26; Zephaniah 3:17
Facing financial need	1 John 5:14–15; 1 Timothy 6:6–10
When friends fail	Psalm 41:9–13; Luke 17:3–4; 2 Timothy 4:16–18
If God seems distant	Psalm 139
In grief	Psalm 34:18; John 11:25–26; 1 Thessalonians 4:13–18
Guilty of sin	Psalm 51; Psalm 32
When I'm lonely	Psalm 23; 2 Timothy 4:16–18
In need of rest	Psalm 91:1–4
In times of sorrow	Matthew 5:4; 2 Corinthians 1:3–5
When I suffer	Psalm 34:19; John 16:33; Romans 8:16–17
In temptation	1 Corinthians 10:13; 1 Peter 5:8–11; Hebrews 4:15–16
In thanksgiving	Psalm 100
In times of weakness	Psalm 46
For the weary	1 Corinthians 15:58; Galatians 6:9–10
When I'm worried	Philippians 4:6–7; Psalm 94:17–19; Matthew 6:19–21

IDENTIFICATION

Name

Street

City

Phone   Cell Phone

E-mail Address

In case of emergency or illness notify:

Name

Street

City

Phone

Copyright © 2011 CTA, Inc., 1625 Larkin Williams Rd.,
Fenton, MO 63026   www.CTAinc.com

Unless otherwise indicated, Scripture quotations are from The Holy Bible, English
Standard Version, copyright © 2001 by Crossway Bibles, a division of Good News
Publishers. Used by permission. All rights reserved.

Scripture quotations marked NIV are taken from the Holy Bible, New International
Version®, NIV®. Copyright © 1973, 1978, 1984 by Biblica, Inc.™ Used by
permission of Zondervan. All rights reserved worldwide.

Scripture quotations marked NKJV are from the New King James Version. Copyright
© 1982 by Thomas Nelson, Inc. Used by permission. All rights reserved.

Scripture quotations marked KJV are from the King James Version of the Bible.

ISBN 978-1-935404-33-0
Printed in Thailand